THIS **BEN 10 ALIEN FORCE** ANNUAL BELONGS TO

MARTIN PAUL

BEN 10
ALIEN FORCE™

ANNUAL 2010

CONTENTS

EGMONT
We bring stories to life

First published in Great Britain 2009
by Egmont UK Limited, 239 Kensington High Street, London W8 6SA
Created for Egmont by John Brown
Editorial: William Petty Design: Grant Kempster
Cartoon Network, the logo, BEN 10, ⊗ and all related
characters and elements are trademark and © Cartoon Network
(s09)
All rights reserved.

ISBN 978 1 4052 4653 8
1 3 5 7 9 10 8 6 4 2
Printed in Italy

BEN IS BACK!

IT'S BEEN FIVE PEACEFUL YEARS SINCE BEN TENNYSON LAST STRAPPED ON THE OMNITRIX AND WENT ALIEN. BUT EVERYTHING IS ABOUT TO CHANGE ...

NOW GRANDPA MAX HAS GONE MISSING, AND BEN HAS TO DO SOMETHING HE VOWED HE'D NEVER DO AGAIN: GO HERO! BUT THE OMNITRIX HAS CHANGED TOO - NOW THERE ARE TEN NEW ALIENS FOR BEN TO DISCOVER ...

LUCKILY, BEN'S NOT ALONE. COUSIN GWEN IS HERE TO HELP, AND SHE'S GOT SOME PRETTY SPECIAL POWERS OF HER OWN. SO HAS KEVIN LEVIN, ALIAS KEVIN 11 - IF HE CAN JUST LEAVE HIS BAD-BOY PAST BEHIND!

NOW YOU CAN JOIN THE ACTION! READ ABOUT BEN'S ADVENTURES IN GRIPPING COMIC STRIP STORIES, LEARN ALL THERE IS TO KNOW ABOUT HIS FRIENDS AND ENEMIES, AND SOLVE SOME BRAIN-BENDING PUZZLES. AND WHEN YOU THINK YOU'RE READY, SIGN UP TO THE OMNITRIX MISSION ON PAGE 38, AND FIND GRANDPA MAX!

SO WHAT ARE YOU WAITING FOR? TURN OVER AND GET GOING!

BEN 10 ALIEN FORCE

BEN TENNYSON

BEN TENNYSON IS BACK! AND THIS TIME HE'S OLDER AND WISER. WITH A NEWLY CONFIGURED OMNITRIX, BEN HAS TEN BRAND-NEW AWESOME ALIENS TO MASTER AND UTILISE IN MORE INTERGALACTIC ADVENTURES!

STRENGTHS

BEN HAS GREAT INNER STRENGTH AND HE RECOGNISES THE VALUE OF TRUE FRIENDSHIP. THIS IS WHY HE HAS BEEN ENTRUSTED WITH THE MIGHTY OMNITRIX.

WHEN IT COMES TO HELPING THOSE IN NEED, HE NEVER HESITATES AND HE NEVER GIVES UP; HIS COURAGE IS SECOND TO NONE. HIS REPUTATION IS LEGENDARY AND ALREADY SPREADS FAR BEYOND THIS SOLAR SYSTEM.

WEAKNESSES

IN HIS RUSH TO HELP OTHERS, BEN CAN BE HASTY AND IMPULSIVE. THAT'S WHEN HE MAKES MISTAKES – HE'S ONLY HUMAN, AFTER ALL!

SOMETIMES, BEN DOESN'T BELIEVE IN HIMSELF AS MUCH AS HE SHOULD. LUCKILY, HE'S GOT A GREAT FAMILY BEHIND HIM.

"TECHNICALLY I'M A WHOLE BUNCH OF MONSTERS!"

GWEN TENNYSON

BEN'S COUSIN, GWEN TENNYSON, IS PRETTY COOL ... FOR A GIRL. OVER THE YEARS SHE AND BEN HAVE DROPPED THEIR CHILDISH SQUABBLES AND BECOME FIRM AND LOYAL FRIENDS.

STRENGTHS

GWEN HAS SUPER POWERS OF HER OWN, WHICH SHE HAS LEARNED TO HARNESS AND MANIPULATE OVER TIME. NOW SHE IS A TRULY GUTSY OPPONENT.

SWITCHED ON, FEISTY AND FOCUSED, SHE'S ALWAYS THERE TO OFFER GOOD ADVICE TO HER COUSIN ... AND KEEP THE PEACE BETWEEN HIM AND KEVIN!

WEAKNESSES

SOMETIMES GWEN CAN BE STUBBORN, A TRAIT WHICH CAN HOLD HER BACK AND CLOUD HER JUDGEMENT.

HER DIRECT, NO-NONSENSE MANNER CAN SEEM A BIT BOSSY AT TIMES IF SHE'S NOT CAREFUL.

"CAN'T I LEAVE YOU GUYS ALONE FOR TWO MINUTES?"

SWAMPFIRE

SWAMPFIRE WAS THE FIRST NEW AMAZING ALIEN SPECIES BEN CHOSE TO TRANSFORM INTO WITH HIS REBOOTED OMNITRIX. YUCK! WHAT A STENCH! SWAMPFIRE LOOKS AND SMELLS LIKE A WALKING, ROTTING COMPOST HEAP!

MAKING A STINK ISN'T ONE OF HIS POWERS THOUGH. INSTEAD, HE HAS CONSIDERABLE STRENGTH AND CAN REATTACH SEVERED LIMBS.

SWAMPFIRE CAN ALSO ATTACK FROM AFAR, BY THROWING FLAMEBOLTS AND CONTROLLING PLANT LIFE.

SWAMPFIRE POWER FILE

- SHOOTS FIRE
- REGENERATES
- CONTROLS PLANT LIFE

ROOT ROUTES

SWAMPFIRE HAS GROWN A VINE MAZE TO KEEP GWEN SAFE FROM DNALIEN ATTACK – BUT THERE ARE WAYS TO GET THROUGH! YOU CAN BLOCK OFF FIVE PATHS BY COLOURING IN THE POINTS MARKED ⊙ . WHICH FIVE MUST YOU BLOCK TO PROTECT GWEN?

ANSWERS ON PAGE 58

KEVIN LEVIN

ONE-TIME FOE OF BEN AND GWEN, KEVIN IS NOW UNITED WITH THE TENNYSONS IN THEIR BATTLE AGAINST ALIEN ENEMIES. BUT HAS HE REALLY CHANGED HIS CROOKED WAYS?

STRENGTHS

KEVIN CAN ABSORB THE PROPERTIES OF SOLID SUBSTANCES SUCH AS METAL, WOOD OR STONE – HANDY IN A BATTLE. HE'S THE ONLY ONE OUT OF THE THREE WHO CAN DRIVE, AND HE HAS THE ULTIMATE MUSCLE CAR.

BENEATH HIS BAD-BOY BRAVADO, KEVIN HAS A GOOD HEART. AND AS GWEN FINDS OUT, YOU COULD EVEN CLAIM HE WAS CHARMING ... SOMETIMES!

WEAKNESSES

KEVIN STILL CAN'T HELP BEING SWAYED BY MONEY, THOUGH AT LEAST HE NOW REALISES THERE ARE MORE IMPORTANT THINGS.

BECAUSE OF HIS SHADY PAST, KEVIN FINDS IT HARD TO LOSE HIS UNRELIABLE IMAGE. AND HIS PRIDE CAN SOMETIMES BE AN OBSTACLE, TOO.

"IS THIS WHEN YOU TURN INTO AN ALIEN AND TRY AND KICK MY BUTT?"

MAX TENNYSON

MAX TENNYSON IS BEN AND GWEN'S GRANDFATHER. MAX MAY BE RETIRED NOW, BUT HIS ADVENTUROUS SPIRIT HASN'T WANED ONE BIT. NOW, SAVING THE UNIVERSE IS A HOBBY – OR IT WAS UNTIL HE WENT MISSING ...

STRENGTHS

DESPITE HIS ADVANCING YEARS, MAX IS ALWAYS ON THE BALL. HE'S A SLICK COMBATANT, AGILE AND STEALTHY. A GOOD MAN, RESPECTED THROUGHOUT THE GALAXY, MAX WILL DO ANYTHING TO SAVE HIS FAMILY AND HIS PLANET.

MAX IS A DOTING GRANDFATHER WHO IS VERY PROUD OF HIS FAMILY. HE HAS TAUGHT BEN AND GWEN MOST THINGS THEY KNOW AND HAS GREAT CONFIDENCE IN THEM.

WEAKNESSES

BECAUSE MAX CAUSES TROUBLE FOR THE ALIEN VILLAINS, THEY ARE ALWAYS ON HIS CASE, TRYING TO TRACK HIM DOWN AND ANNIHILATE HIM.

HIS GRANDKIDS GET DRAGGED INTO IT TOO, OF COURSE. GOOD JOB HE'S TRAINED THEM WELL!

"THERE'S A LOT I CAN'T REVEAL YET. YOU CAN'T GO IT ALONE."

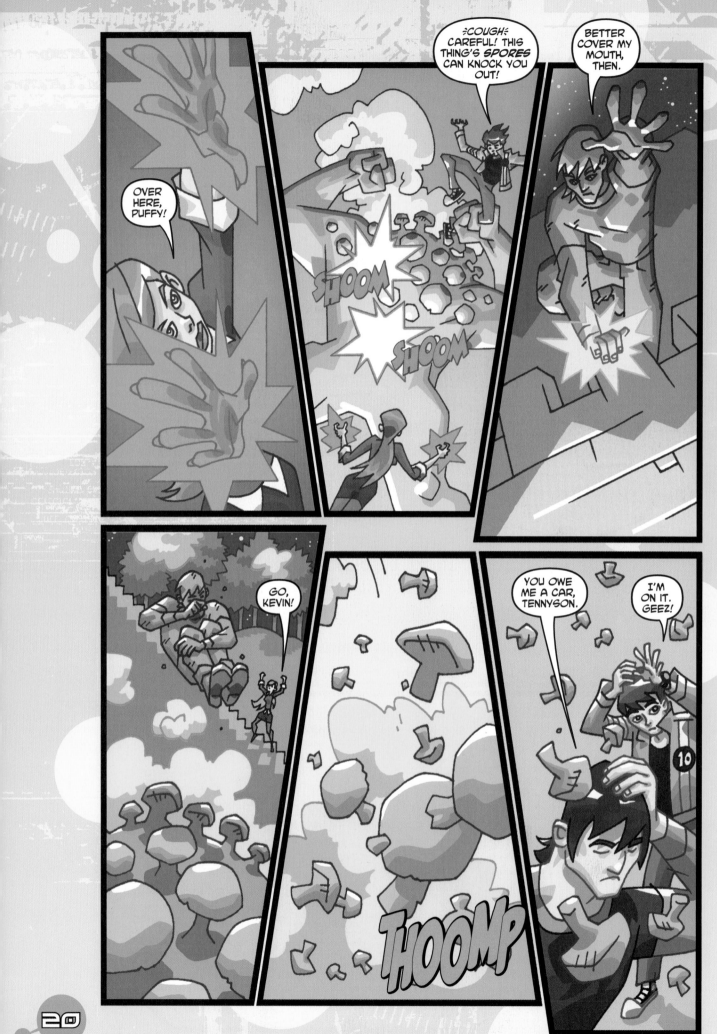

THERE! C'MON!
BEN'S DOWN!
HE CAN TAKE CARE OF HIMSELF. I NEED MY CAR!
WHATEVER.
ZZZNORK ...HUH?
OH, MAN...

THE BAD GUYS
THE HIGHBREED

THE HIGHBREED ARE BELIEVED TO BE THE FIRST EVER INTELLIGENT LIFEFORM IN THE HISTORY OF THE UNIVERSE. THEY CONSIDER THEMSELVES THE ONE TRUE SPECIES. AS FAR AS THEY'RE CONCERNED, ALL OTHER ALIEN BREEDS ARE VERMIN WHO ARE CONTAMINATING THEIR SPACE – ESPECIALLY HUMANS!

THE HIGHBREED ARE FEARLESS AND MERCILESS CREATURES WITH SUPREME STRENGTH. WITH THEIR EVIL AIMS THEY ARE THE WORST THREAT BEN HAS EVER COME ACROSS.

"HUMAN SCUM, I WILL CLEANSE THE WORLD OF YOUR FILTH!"

THEY ARE DETERMINED TO CLEANSE THE UNIVERSE OF OTHER SPECIES, AND EARTH IS THEIR NEXT TARGET!

DNALIENS

THE DNALIENS ARE THE NAMELESS AND FACELESS SERVANTS OF THE HIGHBREED. THEY USE 'IDENTITY MASK' TECHNOLOGY, WHICH ALLOWS THEM TO GO UNDETECTED, DISGUISED AS OTHER BEINGS.

THEIR STRANGE ALIEN WEAPONRY INCLUDES A PRETTY GROSS HABIT – THEY VOMIT UP STICKY GOO AND COVER THEIR ENEMIES IN IT. DNALIENS ALSO HAVE A MASS OF EXTENDABLE TENTACLES THAT THEY USE TO CAPTURE THEIR FOES.

THEY ARE IN A DARK ALLIANCE WITH THE FOREVER KNIGHTS, TRADING ILLEGAL ALIEN TECHNOLOGY.

THE FOREVER KNIGHTS ARE A HUMAN ORGANISATION FORMED IN THE MIDDLE AGES. BACK THEN, THEIR GOAL WAS TO PROTECT THE WORLD FROM ALIEN THREATS. OVER THE CENTURIES THEIR NOBLE PURPOSE BECAME CORRUPTED – INTO CRIMINAL ACTIVITY.

FOREVER KNIGHTS

THEIR QUEST IS TO GAIN ILLEGAL ALIEN TECHNOLOGY FOR THEIR OWN POWER – AND THEY DON'T CARE HOW THEY GO ABOUT IT. THE KNIGHTS WOULD NOT HESITATE TO ERADICATE ANY BEING THAT GOT IN THEIR WAY – APART FROM DNALIENS AND THE HIGHBREED, WHO ARE THEIR ALLIES.

THEIR MOST PRIZED WEAPON IS THE DANGEROUS LEVEL FIVE LASER LANCE!

JET RAY

LIKE A TURBO-BOOSTED MANTA-RAY, JET RAY CAN ZOOM THROUGH THE AIR AND POWER THROUGH WATER AT THE SPEED OF SOUND. BLINK AND YOU JUST MIGHT MISS HIM! ENEMIES BEWARE - HE SHOOTS ENERGY BLASTS FROM HIS EYES.

HE'S GOT QUITE A STING IN HIS TAIL, TOO - HE CAN FIRE VIOLENT NEUROSHOCKS WITH THE POWER TO SHUT DOWN AN ATTACKER'S ENTIRE NERVOUS SYSTEM!

JET RAY IS ULTRA-MANOEUVRABLE. HE CAN ZOOM AND DODGE LIKE A TRUE SKYSURFER!

JET RAY POWER FILE

- ULTRA AGILE
- SUPERSONIC SPEED
- SHOOTS NEUROSHOCKS

MOONLIGHT SHADOW

ONLY ONE OF THESE SILHOUETTES IS THE REAL JET RAY. WHICH ONE IS IT?

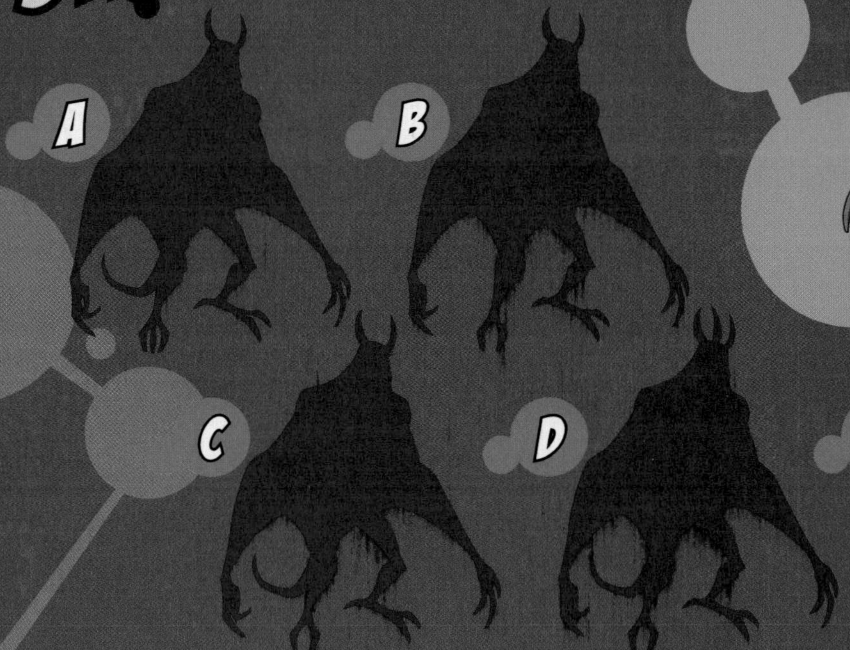

A

B

C

D

E

VICIOUS CIRCLES

BEN AS JET RAY NEEDS TO DO A QUICK AERIAL TOUR OF THESE CROP CIRCLES, LOOKING OUT FOR DNALIENS. IF HE CAN CRACK THE CIRCLES' CODE, HE CAN SAVE SOME TIME.

FIND THE SHORTEST ROUTE WHICH VISITS EACH CIRCLE ONLY ONCE, STARTING AND ENDING AT THE DOUBLE CIRCLE. ADD UP THE DISTANCES TO CHECK.

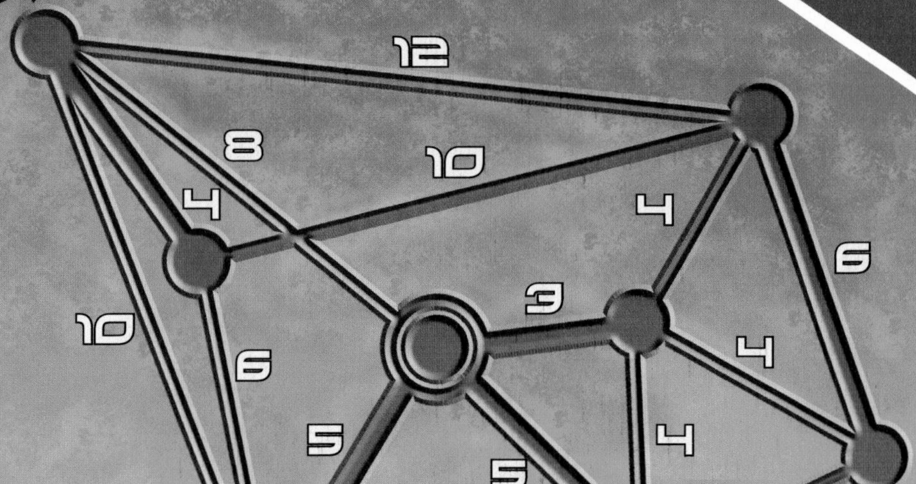

12

8

4

10

4

10

6

3

4

5

4

5

6

4

OMNITRIX TIP

THE SHORTEST ROUTE ALTERNATES BETWEEN THE THICK AND THIN LINES.

25

ANSWERS ON PAGE 68.

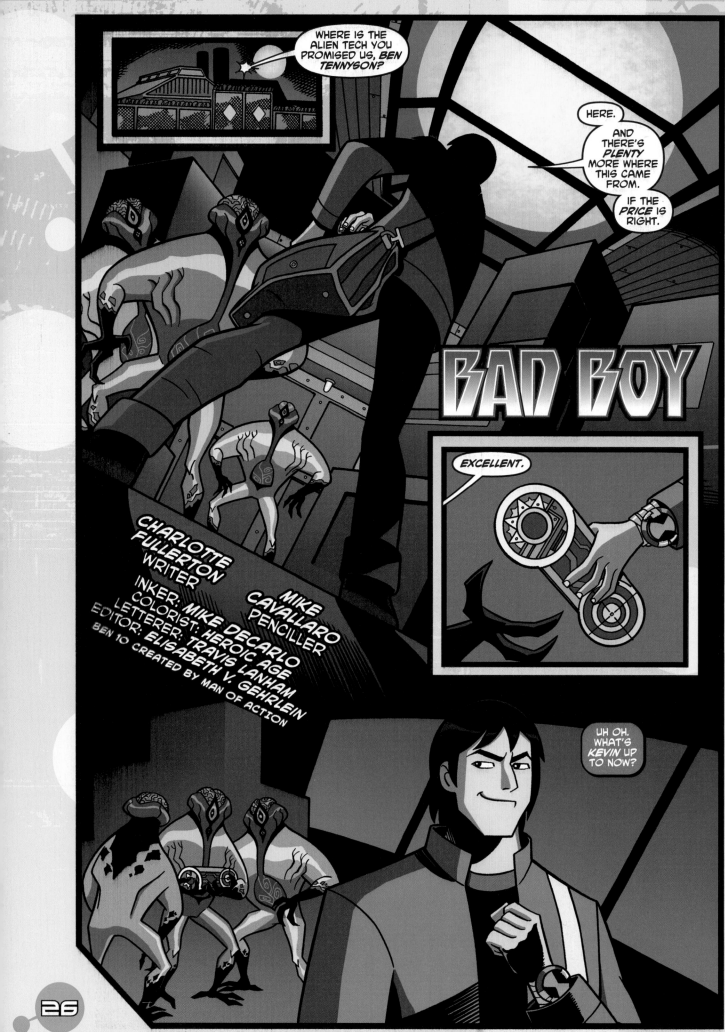

"YOU KNOW, BEN, I WASN'T SURE *HOW* YOU WERE GOING TO TAKE THE NEWS THAT KEVIN HAS TURNED OUT TO BE SO *UNTRUSTWORTHY.*"

"BUT I NEVER WOULD HAVE GUESSED YOU'D BE *HAPPY* ABOUT IT!"

"ARE YOU JUST TRYING TO RUB IT IN? THAT THE GUY I *LIKE* IS STILL ONE OF THE *BAD* GUYS AFTER ALL?

"'CAUSE THAT'S *REAL* MATURE OF YOU."

I KNOW EXACTLY WHAT KEVIN'S BEEN DOING, GWEN. BECAUSE *I'M* THE ONE WHO PUT HIM UP TO IT!

BEEP BEEP BEEP

GASP

THAT WAS A *SIGNAL* FROM KEVIN! SOMETHING'S GONE WRONG!

TIME FOR THE *REAL BEN TENNYSON* TO SWING INTO ACTION, AS--

SPIDERMONKEY!

DESIGN ALIEN TECH

EVERYBODY WANTS TO GET THEIR HANDS ON AWESOME ALIEN TECHNOLOGY! CAN YOU DESIGN SOMETHING TO TIP THE INTERGALACTIC BALANCE OF POWER IN BEN'S FAVOUR?

TECH NAME:

The Triple razor

WHAT IT DOES:

it Powers ships

HUMUNGOUSAUR

HALF-MAN, HALF-DINOSAUR, HUMUNGOUSAUR IS THE HEAVYWEIGHT CHAMPION OF ALL THE ALIEN HEROES. HE HAS THE ABILITY TO CHANGE SIZE AND CAN GROW UP TO NEARLY 20 METRES TALL, DWARFING HIS FOES.

WITH HIS MEGA MUSCLES, 'HUMUNGO' CAN RIP THROUGH BUILDINGS AS IF THEY WERE MARSHMALLOWS AND TRAMPLE ENEMIES LIKE ANTS UNDERFOOT.

HE CHARGES, HE ROARS, HE OBLITERATES ... THERE'S NO OBSTACLE TOO GREAT FOR THIS GIANT HERO!

HUMUNGOUSAUR POWER FILE

- ⊗ ENDURANCE
- ⊗ CHANGES SIZE
- ⊗ SUPER STRENGTH

HUMUNGO-SEARCH

WHEN YOU'VE CONQUERED THIS HUMUNGOUS WORDSEARCH, READ DOWN THE 13TH COLUMN, AND WRITE DOWN EVERY 2ND UNUSED LETTER. THEN UNSCRAMBLE THEM TO REVEAL SOMETHING THAT HUMUNGOUSAUR HAS A LOT OF.

U	X	X	A	M	Z	D	J	V	E	R	R	I	F
Y	A	B	D	C	R	Q	C	Z	C	U	L	O	D
H	U	M	U	N	G	O	U	S	A	U	R	S	L
X	Q	E	O	N	A	X	T	E	X	E	Q	J	L
J	N	I	V	E	K	L	C	S	V	F	D	M	I
W	G	O	E	T	O	H	I	E	N	S	N	O	H
G	Y	E	K	N	O	M	R	E	D	I	P	S	C
W	Z	X	E	E	O	K	N	E	N	L	A	U	G
B	D	W	C	B	N	T	E	I	U	S	X	R	I
S	G	H	J	I	B	R	S	M	T	N	B	K	B
P	O	O	G	Z	B	I	B	A	E	R	N	L	Y
E	A	H	Q	H	N	E	R	I	M	A	I	X	G
Z	T	P	G	X	R	G	L	K	I	O	U	X	J
S	L	I	I	S	W	A	M	P	F	I	R	E	H
G	H	E	R	O	T	I	M	E	N	C	T	H	I
J	S	H	U	Y	B	C	H	S	V	R	W	E	C
A	J	D	O	R	V	Q	R	O	A	N	U	Y	X
H	G	I	N	I	X	J	T	Y	Z	Y	M	C	B

ALIEN X
BEN TEN
BIG CHILL
BRAIN STORM
CHROMASTONE
DNALIENS
ECHO ECHO
FOREVER KNIGHTS
GOOP
GWEN
HERO TIME
HIGHBREED
HUMUNGOUSAUR
JET RAY
KEVIN
MAX
OMNITRIX
PLUMBERS
SPIDERMONKEY
SWAMPFIRE

HUMUNGOUSAUR HAS A LOT OF ...

▱▱▱▱▱▱▱

WRITE THE LETTERS IN HERE

IT'S HERO TIME!
BiG CHiLL

BIG CHILL MAY LEAVE HIS ENEMIES FEELING COLD, BUT HE'S ONE OF BEN 10'S FAVOURITE HEROES. HE HAS TWO FORMS: A REGULAR SOLID FORM AND A FREAKY GHOST-LIKE FORM, WHICH CAN PASS STRAIGHT THROUGH OBJECTS AND BEINGS. CREEPY OR WHAT?

HE CAN BLAST OUT ICY GUSTS POWERFUL ENOUGH TO TAKE OUT HIS OPPONENTS AND HE HAS THE ABILITY TO FREEZE ANYTHING HE CHOOSES.

WHAT'S MORE, BIG CHILL ISN'T INJURED BY ENEMY FIRE – IT JUST GOES RIGHT THROUGH HIM!

BiG CHiLL
POWER FILE
- BLASTS ICE
- TURNS INVISIBLE
- SPECTRAL FORM

BIG FILL

BIG CHILL HAS GONE ALL CREEPY ON US AGAIN — PARTS OF HIM HAVE DISAPPEARED! USE THE NUMBERS TO MATCH THE MISSING PIECES TO THE PICTURE BELOW.

FLAKE OUT!

TAKE A REAL CLOSE LOOK AT SOME ICE! CAN YOU SPOT THREE IDENTICAL SNOWFLAKES?

ANSWERS ON PAGE 68.

OMNITRIX MISSION

GRANDPA MAX IS MISSING, AND IT'S UP TO YOU TO
FIND HIM! IF YOU THINK YOU CAN HANDLE IT, FOLLOW
THE CLUES HE'S HIDDEN THROUGHOUT THIS BOOK, FILL
IN THE ANSWERS, AND GO GET GRANDPA! START BY
TURNING BACK 13 PAGES ...

1. AH, A NICE RELAXING FIELD OF WHEAT! BUT YOU'VE
NO TIME TO REST – ADD UP ALL THE LENGTHS OF
THE THICK PATHS LEADING TO THE DOUBLE CIRCLE,
THEN SUBTRACT THE LENGTH OF THE THIN PATH.
NOW TURN 26 PAGES FORWARDS FROM THAT PAGE ...

2. WELL, IF YOUR BRAIN'S STILL WORKING AFTER
THAT, ANSWER ME THIS: WHAT'S THE 4TH
LETTER OF THE 6TH WORD OF THE 2ND LINE
OF THE 8TH QUESTION?
NOW TURN 10 PAGES BACKWARDS FROM THAT PAGE ...

3. WELL NOW, ON REFLECTION (ON REFLECTION?
GET IT?) LET'S COUNT UP ALL THE MIRRORS
KNIGHT 3 WILL HIT WITH HIS LASER
BEAM WHICH ARE ANGLED LIKE THIS:
NOW TURN 22 PAGES FORWARDS FROM THAT PAGE ...

4. STOP STUMBLING IN THE DARK, THERE'S WORK
TO DO! HOW MANY DEAD ENDS ARE THERE
IN THAT DARKENED ROOM? AND IF 1=A, WHAT
LETTER DOES THAT NUMBER GIVE YOU?
NOW TURN 52 PAGES BACKWARDS FROM THAT PAGE ...

5. DON'T WORRY, WE'LL UNTANGLE THIS RIDDLE.
COUNT UP THE OMNITRIX SYMBOLS YOU HAVEN'T
COLOURED, ADD IT TO THE NUMBER OF WAYS INTO
THE MAZE, AND SUBTRACT THE NUMBER OF HEADS.
NOW TURN 42 PAGES FORWARDS FROM THAT PAGE ...

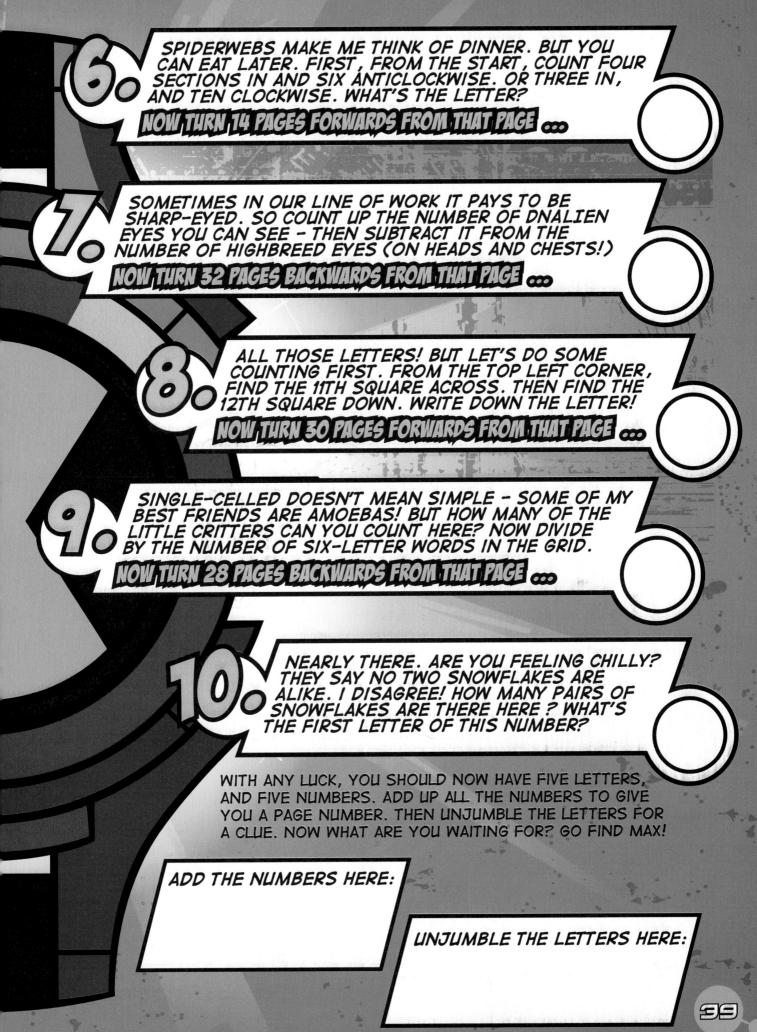

6. SPIDERWEBS MAKE ME THINK OF DINNER. BUT YOU CAN EAT LATER. FIRST, FROM THE START, COUNT FOUR SECTIONS IN AND SIX ANTICLOCKWISE. OR THREE IN, AND TEN CLOCKWISE. WHAT'S THE LETTER?

NOW TURN 14 PAGES FORWARDS FROM THAT PAGE ...

7. SOMETIMES IN OUR LINE OF WORK IT PAYS TO BE SHARP-EYED. SO COUNT UP THE NUMBER OF DNALIEN EYES YOU CAN SEE – THEN SUBTRACT IT FROM THE NUMBER OF HIGHBREED EYES (ON HEADS AND CHESTS!)

NOW TURN 32 PAGES BACKWARDS FROM THAT PAGE ...

8. ALL THOSE LETTERS! BUT LET'S DO SOME COUNTING FIRST. FROM THE TOP LEFT CORNER, FIND THE 11TH SQUARE ACROSS. THEN FIND THE 12TH SQUARE DOWN. WRITE DOWN THE LETTER!

NOW TURN 30 PAGES FORWARDS FROM THAT PAGE ...

9. SINGLE-CELLED DOESN'T MEAN SIMPLE – SOME OF MY BEST FRIENDS ARE AMOEBAS! BUT HOW MANY OF THE LITTLE CRITTERS CAN YOU COUNT HERE? NOW DIVIDE BY THE NUMBER OF SIX-LETTER WORDS IN THE GRID.

NOW TURN 28 PAGES BACKWARDS FROM THAT PAGE ...

10. NEARLY THERE. ARE YOU FEELING CHILLY? THEY SAY NO TWO SNOWFLAKES ARE ALIKE. I DISAGREE! HOW MANY PAIRS OF SNOWFLAKES ARE THERE HERE ? WHAT'S THE FIRST LETTER OF THIS NUMBER?

WITH ANY LUCK, YOU SHOULD NOW HAVE FIVE LETTERS, AND FIVE NUMBERS. ADD UP ALL THE NUMBERS TO GIVE YOU A PAGE NUMBER. THEN UNJUMBLE THE LETTERS FOR A CLUE. NOW WHAT ARE YOU WAITING FOR? GO FIND MAX!

ADD THE NUMBERS HERE:

UNJUMBLE THE LETTERS HERE:

39

ANSWERS ON PAGE 69.

IT'S HERO TIME!
CHROMASTONE

BEING A LIVING STONE MIGHT NOT SOUND THAT EXCITING, BUT THINK AGAIN ... MADE UP OF CRYSTAL COMPOUNDS, CHROMASTONE IS VIRTUALLY INDESTRUCTIBLE, MAKING HIM ONE ROCK-HARD ALIEN!

HIS CRYSTAL BODY ABSORBS AND DEFLECTS ENERGY, LASERS, RADIATION AND ELECTRICITY. SO ANYTHING SHOT AT HIM CAN BE SENT BACK IN THE DIRECTION IT CAME FROM!

CHROMASTONE DOESN'T RELY ON OTHER PEOPLE'S FIREPOWER, THOUGH – HE FIRES HIS OWN LASER RAYS TOO!

CHROMASTONE
POWER FILE
- ✗ INDESTRUCTIBLE
- ✗ ABSORBS RAYS
- ✗ SHOOTS LASERS

CRAZY LASERS

THE FOREVER KNIGHTS ARE TRYING TO USE THE MIRRORS TO BLAST KEVIN WITH THEIR LASERS! WHICH KNIGHT'S BEAM SHOULD CHROMASTONE BLOCK TO STOP KEVIN GETTING FRIED? AND WHICH KNIGHT IS GOING TO HIT ONE OF HIS OWN COMRADES?

OMNITRIX TIP

DRAW IN THE PATHS OF THE LASERS TO SEE WHERE THEY GO.

1

2

3

4

LASERS BOUNCE OFF MIRRORS LIKE THIS:

ANSWERS ON PAGE 69

BRAIN STORM

THIS CRAB-LIKE ALIEN HAS A MIGHTY SHELL AND FEARSOME CLAWS, BUT BRAIN STORM'S BIGGEST WEAPON IS HIS BULGING BRAIN, OF COURSE. WHEN BRAIN STORM PUTS HIS MIND TO IT, HE CAN CONQUER ANYTHING!

BRAIN STORM IS NOT JUST VERY CLEVER, HE ALSO USES HIS BRAIN TO FIRE ENERGY FUNNELS AND CREATE PROTECTIVE FORCE FIELDS ...

... NOT FORGETTING THE ELECTROMAGNETIC STORMS HE CAN WHIP UP TO VAPORISE ANYTHING IN HIS PATH!

BRAIN STORM POWER FILE
- ENERGY FUNNELS
- STORM ACTIVATOR
- SUPER INTELLIGENCE

BRAIN DRAIN

1 WHICH WEIGHS MORE – A TONNE OF CANDYFLOSS, OR A TONNE OF TITANIUM?

2 IF MY NEIGHBOUR'S ROOSTER LAYS AN EGG IN MY GARDEN, WHO DOES THE EGG BELONG TO?

3 THE 22ND AND 24TH PRESIDENTS OF THE UNITED STATES HAD THE SAME PARENTS, BUT THEY WEREN'T BROTHERS. HOW COME?

4 BEFORE MT. EVEREST WAS DISCOVERED, WHAT WAS THE HIGHEST MOUNTAIN IN THE WORLD?

5 IS IT LEGAL FOR A MAN TO MARRY HIS WIDOW'S SISTER?

6 YOU'RE DRIVING A BUS WITH 8 PEOPLE ON BOARD. AT THE 1ST STOP, 3 GET OFF. AT THE 2ND STOP, 6 GET ON. AT THE 3RD, 5 GET OFF. WHAT'S THE NAME OF THE DRIVER?

7 WHO WROTE BEETHOVEN'S FIFTH SYMPHONY?

8 MRS GREEN LIVES IN A PINK BUNGALOW. THE CURTAINS ARE BLUE, THE CHAIRS ARE YELLOW, AND THE DOORS ARE ORANGE. WHAT COLOUR ARE THE STAIRS?

9 A ROPE LADDER WITH SIX RUNGS HANGS FROM THE SIDE OF A BOAT, WITH THE BOTTOM RUNG ON THE WATER. THE RUNGS ARE 50CM APART, AND THE TIDE RISES BY ONE METRE AN HOUR. HOW LONG UNTIL ALL THE RUNGS ARE COVERED?

10 HOW MANY BRICKS DOES IT TAKE TO COMPLETE A SKYSCRAPER MADE ENTIRELY OF BRICKS?

ANSWERS ON PAGE 68.

IT'S HERO TIME!
SPIDERMONKEY

WITH THE AGILITY OF A MONKEY AND THE WEB-SPINNING SKILLS OF A SPIDER, THIS IS ONE HERO TO RECKON WITH. THE MULTI-LIMBED SPIDERMONKEY CAN STICK TO WALLS AND SWING AROUND ON WEBLINES, OUTWITTING HIS FOES AS HE GOES.

WHEN IT COMES TO CAPTURING HIS ENEMIES, SPIDERMONKEY HAS IT COVERED ... HE COVERS THEM IN HIS GIANT WEBS, LEAVING THEM TIED UP AND POWERLESS.

AND HE'S NO SOFTY EITHER ... HIS SPIDERWEBS ARE AS HARD AS STEEL CABLE!

SPIDERMONKEY
POWER FILE

- ⊗ STICKS TO WALLS
- ⊗ SPINS GIANT WEBS
- ⊗ SUPERHUMAN AGILITY

WEB PAGE

CAN YOU FIND A WAY THROUGH SPIDERMONKEY'S WEB? WHEN YOU HAVE, WRITE DOWN ALL THE LETTERS THE ROUTE PASSES THROUGH. THEN CROSS OUT EVERY LETTER THAT APPEARS TWICE TO SPELL OUT THE NAME OF BEN'S OTHER COUSIN.

START

FINISH

J N K T D W L T
I T Z D N G F C
D L A K R C I
U D A R S E G L

WRITE THE LETTERS YOU PASS THROUGH IN HERE

BEN'S OTHER COUSIN IS:

Ken

ANSWERS ON PAGE 69.

55

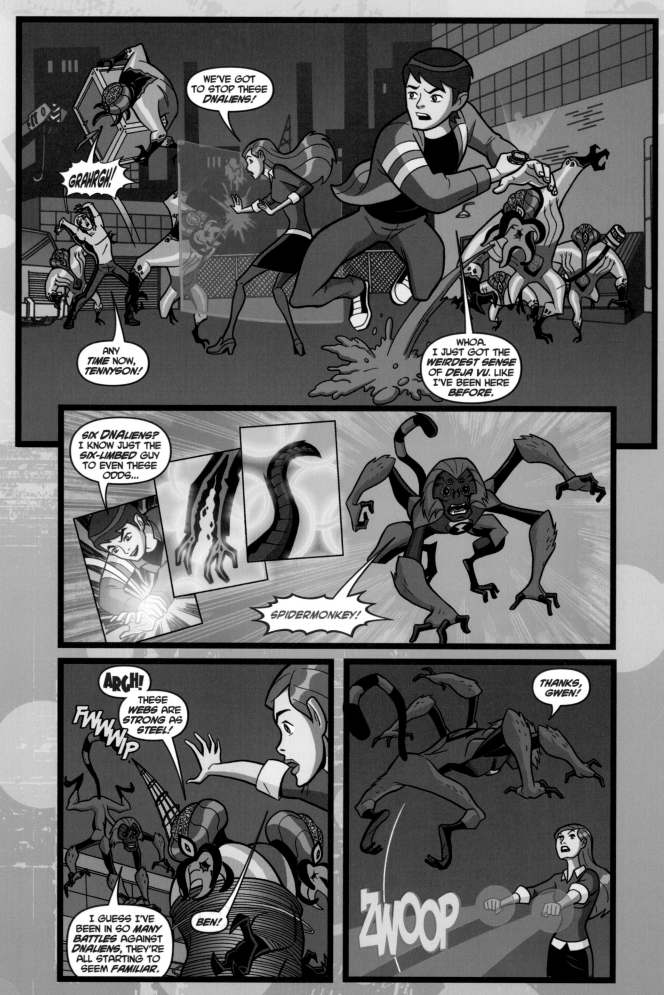

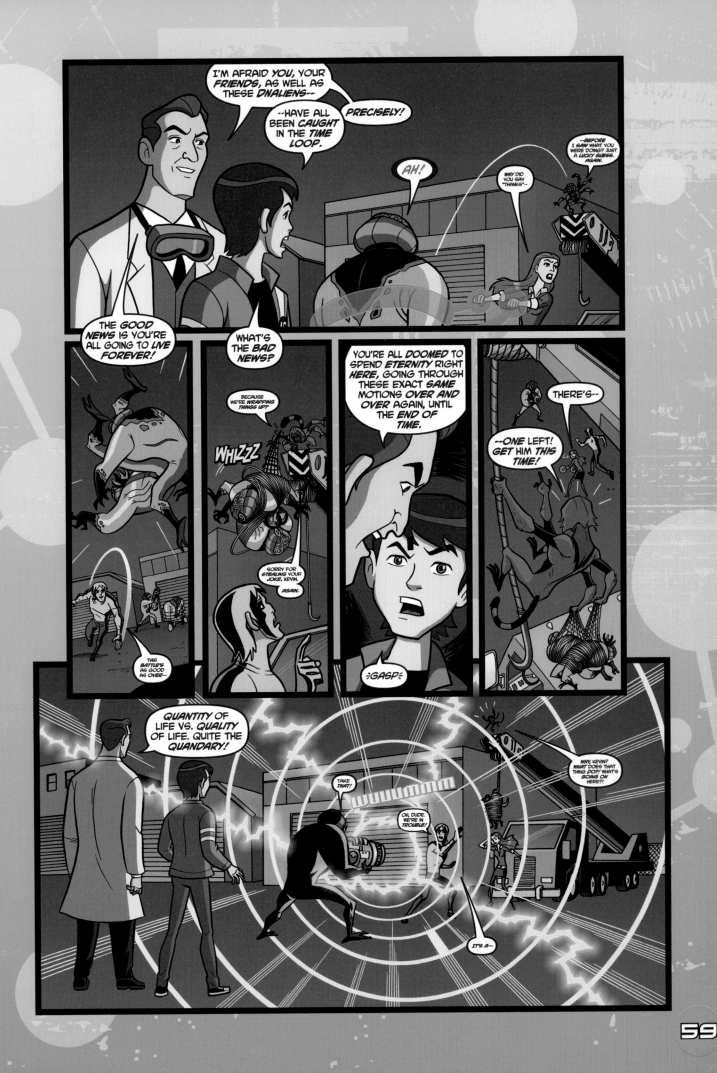

FWWWNIP
ARGH!
THESE WEBS ARE STRONG AS STEEL!
WHY, THANK YOU FOR NOTICING.
I MADE THEM MYSELF. CHUCKLE
BEN!
ZWOOP
HEY! WATCH IT, GWEN!
I MEAN, NICE SHOT, GWEN!
AH!
THIS BATTLE'S AS GOOD AS OVER!
BECAUSE WE'RE WRAPPING THINGS UP! SNERK
WHIZZZ
HA HA! I COULD DO THIS ALL DAY!
THERE'S ONE LEFT! GET HIM!
TAKE THAT!
WUUUMMM
OH, DUDE. WE'RE IN TROUBLE!
WHY? WHAT DOES THAT THING DO?
IT'S A--

ECHO ECHO

ECHO ECHO IS A WALKING AMPLIFIER WHO PACKS ONE POWERFUL PUNCH! HE CAN DELIVER A WALL OF SOUND WITH ENOUGH EAR-SPLITTING ENERGY TO SHATTER STEEL AND STOP ANY ATTACKER IN ITS TRACKS.

HE MIGHT BE SMALL, BUT ECHO ECHO MAKES UP FOR IT IN NUMBERS ... HE CAN DUPLICATE HIMSELF, CREATING A SMALL ARMY OF ALIEN CLONES.

ECHO ECHO CAN AMPLIFY OTHER SOUNDS, AND CAN USE HIS SONIC PULSES AS A RADAR.

ECHO ECHO
POWER FILE
- MULTIPLIES
- SONIC POWER
- AMPLIFIES SOUND

PHONEY CLONES

ECHO ECHO HAS DUPLICATED HIMSELF TO LAUNCH A SONIC ATTACK ON THE FOREVER KNIGHTS. BUT ONLY TWO OF THESE ECHO ECHOES ARE EXACT REPLICAS. CAN YOU SPOT WHICH TWO ARE FOR REAL AND WHICH ONES ARE PHONEY CLONES?

A   B   C   D

E   F   G   H

ECHOLOCATION ECHOLOCATION

BEN'S BEEN LEFT IN THE DARK, BUT LUCKILY HE CAN USE ECHOLOCATION TO FIND HIS WAY. COLOUR IN ALL THE SQUARES WITH ⊙ OR ▮▮, THEN FIND YOUR WAY FROM START TO FINISH.

FINISH

START

63

ANSWERS ON PAGE 68

GOOP

THINGS ARE ABOUT TO GET MESSY! GOOP IS A GOOEY, SLIMY, OOZING SINGLE-CELLED ALIEN THAT CAN CHANGE HIS BODY SHAPE INTO ANYTHING. A SMALL FLYING SAUCER FLIES ABOVE HIM CONTROLLING HIS SHAPE-SHIFTING AT ALL TIMES.

AMAZINGLY, GOOP CAN RE-POOL AND REFORM AFTER ALMOST ANY INJURY. AND HE CAN COVER HIS ENEMIES IN GOO, TOO!

IF ALL ELSE FAILS, GOOP HAS THE ABILITY TO SHOOT A HIGHLY CORROSIVE ACID ... SO WATCH OUT!

GOOP POWER FILE

- SHOOTS ACID
- CHANGES SHAPE
- CAN RE-POOL

GOOPY GRID!

WITH HIS AMAZING OOZING ABILITY TO CHANGE SHAPE, GOOP CAN FIT IN ANYWHERE. BUT CAN YOU FIT THESE SLIMY WORDS INTO THE GUNKY GRID BELOW? TWO HAVE BEEN DONE FOR YOU ...

3 LETTERS
GEL
4 LETTERS
GLOB
GUNK
MESS
OOZE
POOL
POUR
5 LETTERS
GOOEY
GROSS
SLIME
SLUSH
SOGGY
~~SPLAT~~
6 LETTERS
PLASMA
~~SPLASH~~
STICKY
7 LETTERS
SQUEEZE
STRETCH
8 LETTERS
SLIPPERY

NUCLEUS FAMILY

LOOK AT THIS JUMBLE OF OVERLAPPING SINGLE-CELLED AMOEBAS. EACH ONE HAS A RED NUCLEUS - EXCEPT ONE. WHICH ONE?

IT'S HERO TIME!
ALIEN X

ALIEN X IS THE MOST POWERFUL AND MYSTERIOUS OF ALL BEN'S ALIENS – HE CAN DO *ANYTHING* JUST BY THINKING IT. BUT IT'S NOT AS EASY AS IT SOUNDS ...

INSIDE THE STAR-FILLED VOID OF ALIEN X'S MIND SIT TWO BEINGS: SERENA (THE VOICE OF LOVE AND COMPASSION) AND BELICUS (THE VOICE OF RAGE AND AGGRESSION). ALIEN X CAN DO *NOTHING* UNTIL THESE TWO AGREE ON IT ...

... AND GETTING THEM TO AGREE IS SOMETHING EVEN BEN HAS DIFFICULTY WITH!

ALIEN X
POWER FILE

- ALL-POWERFUL
- ALTERS SPACE & TIME
- ENDLESS CAPABILITIES

X-CHANGE

ALIEN X CAN DO ANYTHING HE PUTS HIS MIND TO. HE HAS MADE 10 CHANGES TO THE SCENE BELOW. CAN YOU SPOT THEM ALL?

ANSWERS ON PAGE 69

BEN 10 ALIEN FORCE ANSWERS

P 11 ROOT ROUTES

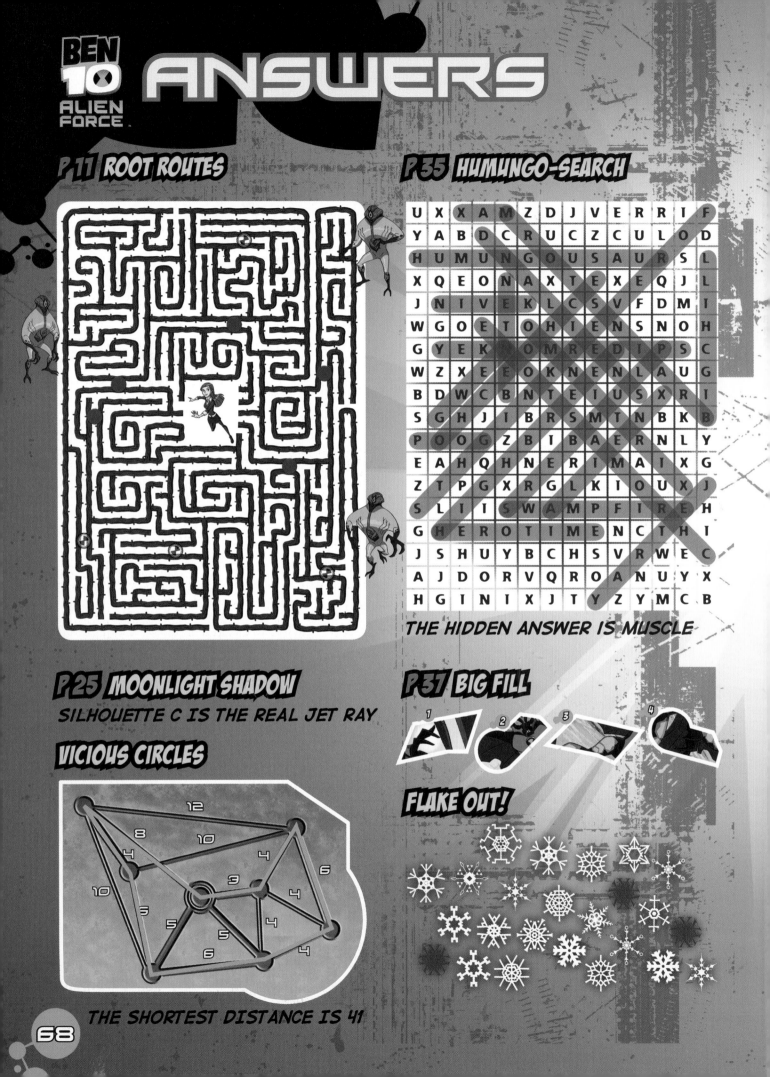

P 35 HUMUNGO-SEARCH

U	X	X	A	M	Z	D	J	V	E	R	R	I	F
Y	A	B	D	C	R	U	C	Z	C	U	L	O	D
H	U	M	U	N	G	O	U	S	A	U	R	S	L
X	Q	E	O	N	A	X	T	E	X	E	Q	J	L
J	N	I	V	E	K	L	C	S	V	F	D	M	I
W	G	O	E	T	O	H	I	E	N	S	N	O	H
G	Y	E	K	O	M	R	E	D	I	P	S	C	
W	Z	X	E	E	O	K	N	E	N	L	A	U	G
B	D	W	C	B	N	T	E	I	U	S	X	R	I
S	G	H	J	I	B	R	S	M	T	N	B	K	B
P	O	O	G	Z	B	I	B	A	E	R	N	L	Y
E	A	H	Q	H	N	E	R	I	M	A	I	X	G
Z	T	P	G	X	R	G	L	K	I	O	U	X	J
S	L	I	I	S	W	A	M	P	F	I	R	E	H
G	H	E	R	O	T	I	M	E	N	C	T	H	I
J	S	H	U	Y	B	C	H	S	V	R	W	E	C
A	J	D	O	R	V	Q	R	O	A	N	U	Y	X
H	G	I	N	I	X	J	T	Y	Z	Y	M	C	B

THE HIDDEN ANSWER IS MUSCLE

P 25 MOONLIGHT SHADOW

SILHOUETTE C IS THE REAL JET RAY

VICIOUS CIRCLES

THE SHORTEST DISTANCE IS 41

P 37 BIG FILL

FLAKE OUT!

P41 CRAZY LASERS

KNIGHT 4 WILL HIT KEVIN.
KNIGHT 3 WILL HIT A KNIGHT.

P51 BRAIN DRAIN

1. THEY BOTH WEIGH THE SAME.
2. NEITHER - ROOSTERS DON'T LAY EGGS.
3. THEY WERE THE SAME PERSON.
4. IT WAS STILL MT. EVEREST.
5. NO - IF A MAN HAS A WIDOW, HE IS DEAD.
6. WHATEVER YOUR NAME IS - YOU'RE THE DRIVER.
7. BEETHOVEN.
8. BUNGALOWS DON'T HAVE STAIRS.
9. NEVER - THE LADDER WILL RISE WITH THE BOAT AS THE WATER LEVEL RISES.
10. JUST ONE - THE LAST ONE.

P53 WEB PAGE

BEN'S OTHER COUSIN IS KEN

P38-39 OMNITRIX MISSION

1. 5 (13-8)
2. L (YELLOW)
3. 7
4. G (7)
5. 5 (4+5-4)
6. S
7. 9 (14-5)
8. A
9. 4 (12÷3)
10. S (SIX)

THE CLUE IS 'GLASS'. MAX IS HIDDEN IN THE WINDOW, ON PAGE 30.

P63 PHONEY CLONES

C AND F ARE THE SAME.

ECHOLOCATION ECHOLOCATION

FINISH

START

P65 GOOPY GRID!

NUCLEUS FAMILY

P67 X-CHANGE